Date: 2/28/20

J GRA 741.5 LUN V.7
Krosoczka, Jarrett.
Lunch Lady and the mutant
mathletes.

"Where the city's brightest go head to head in a math frenzy!"

"These students have fought hard all season long."

"And they're here tonight to win the title!"

Looks like *these* public-school kids won!

Smoke Can of Peas

CLINK~

CLINK~

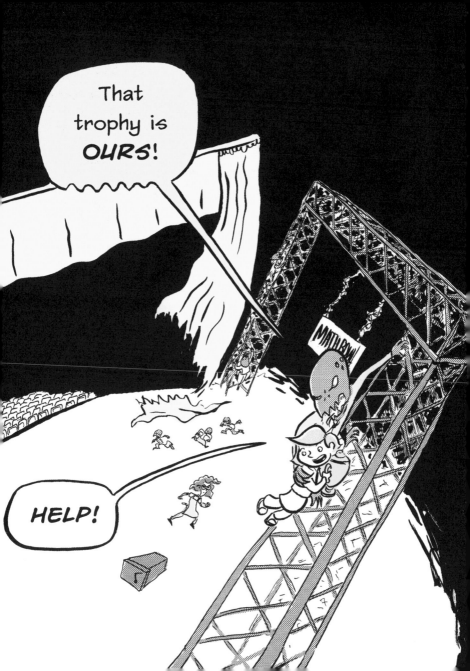

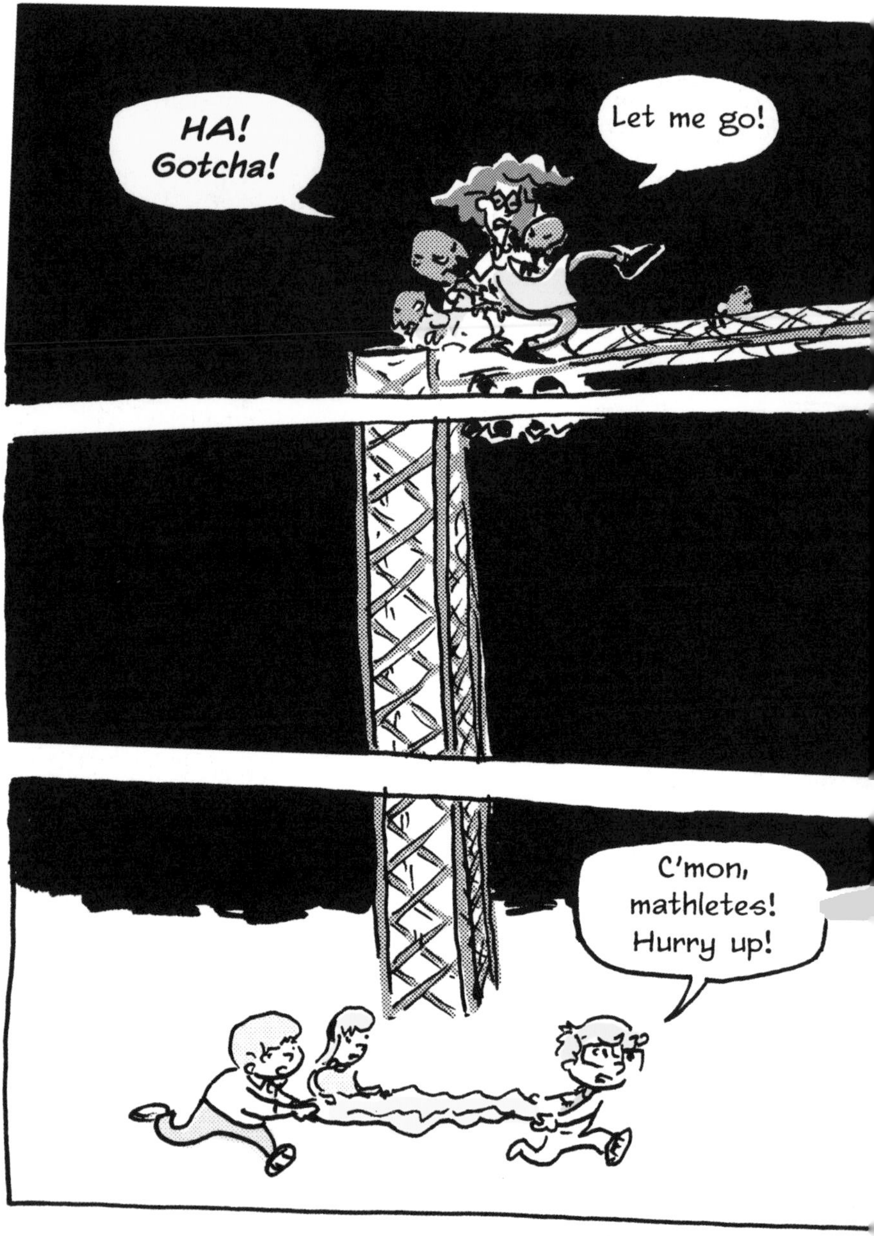
HA! Gotcha!
Let me go!
C'mon, mathletes! Hurry up!

FOR SIOBHÁN AND PETER

The author would like to acknowledge the color assist in this book by Joey Weiser and Michele Chidester.

THIS IS A BORZOI BOOK PUBLISHED BY ALFRED A. KNOPF

Visit us on the Web! rhcbooks.com

Educators and librarians, for a variety of teaching tools, visit us at randomhouse.com/teachers

Library of Congress Cataloging-in-Publication Data
Krosoczka, Jarrett.
Lunch Lady and the mutant mathletes / Jarrett Krosoczka. — 1st ed.
p. cm.
"A Borzoi Book."
Summary: For having skipped the school field trip, Dee, Hector, and Terrence must join the mathletes team, but as they are poised to beat the undefeated champions, secret crime fighter Lunch Lady discovers something strange about the opposing team.
ISBN 978-0-375-87028-6 (trade pbk.) — ISBN 978-0-375-97028-3 (lib. bdg.)
1. Graphic novels. [1. Graphic novels. 2. Competition (Psychology)—Fiction.
3. Mathematics—Fiction. 4. Schools—Fiction. 5. Mystery and detective stories.] I. Title.
PZ7.7.K76Lum 2012
741.5'973—dc23
2011025425

The text of this book is set in Hedge Backwards.
The illustrations were created using ink on paper and digital coloring.

MANUFACTURED IN MALAYSIA
March 2012
10

First Edition